3 2170 02100040 4

K

Thomas Aquinas

Lynn Thorndike

D1451282

KING Township
PUBLIC LIBRARY

Kessinger Publishing's Rare Reprints

Thousands of Scarce and Hard-to-Find Books
on These and other Subjects!

- Americana
- Ancient Mysteries
- Animals
- Anthropology
- Architecture
- Arts
- Astrology
- Bibliographies
- Biographies & Memoirs
- Body, Mind & Spirit
- Business & Investing
- Children & Young Adult
- Collectibles
- Comparative Religions
- Crafts & Hobbies
- Earth Sciences
- Education
- Ephemera
- Fiction
- Folklore
- Geography
- Health & Diet
- History
- Hobbies & Leisure
- Humor
- Illustrated Books
- Language & Culture
- Law
- Life Sciences

- Literature
- Medicine & Pharmacy
- Metaphysical
- Music
- Mystery & Crime
- Mythology
- Natural History
- Outdoor & Nature
- Philosophy
- Poetry
- Political Science
- Science
- Psychiatry & Psychology
- Reference
- Religion & Spiritualism
- Rhetoric
- Sacred Books
- Science Fiction
- Science & Technology
- Self-Help
- Social Sciences
- Symbolism
- Theatre & Drama
- Theology
- Travel & Explorations
- War & Military
- Women
- Yoga
- *Plus Much More!*

We kindly invite you to view our catalog list at:
http://www.kessinger.net

THIS ARTICLE WAS EXTRACTED FROM THE BOOK:

The History of Magic and Experimental Science V4

BY THIS AUTHOR:

Lynn Thorndike

ISBN 0766144399

READ MORE ABOUT THE BOOK AT OUR WEB SITE:

http://www.kessinger.net

KESSINGER
PUBLISHING

OR ORDER THE COMPLETE
BOOK FROM YOUR FAVORITE STORE

ISBN 0766144399

Because this article has been extracted from a parent book, it may have non-pertinent text at the beginning or end of it.

Any blank pages following the article are necessary for our book production requirements. The article herein is complete.

CHAPTER LX

THOMAS AQUINAS

THOMAS AQUINAS was perhaps not so precocious a genius as some of his fellow-countrymen who were artists during the Italian Renaissance. But if he did not die quite as young as Masaccio or Raphael, he nevertheless produced a vast amount of learned writing within a comparatively short time.

Precociousness of Aquinas.

Bibliographical Note. A critical biography of Aquinas has not yet appeared. D. Prümmer began in 1911 to publish the sources, when he edited the hitherto unprinted biography by Peter Calo who wrote about 1300: *Fontes Vitae S. Thomae Aquinatis notis historicis et criticis illustrati,* Fasc. I, Toulouse, 1911. Peter Calo seems to have admitted a great deal of legendary material. D. J. Kennedy's "Thomas Aquinas" in CE profits by this publication and contains perhaps as good a brief sketch of Aquinas' career as there is in English. It also has a good bibliography. It is, however, at variance on some points with Thomas of Cantimpré's statements, as I have indicated in the text.

On the bibliography of Aquinas' own works one may consult: C. U. J. Chevalier, *Catalogue critique des œuvres de Saint Thomas d'Aquin,* 1887; A. Miola, *Codices MSS operum S. Thomae de Aquino et S. Bonaventurae in Regia Neapolitana Bibliotheca,* 1874; P. Mandonnet, *Des Écrits Authentiques de S. Thomas d'Aquin,* Fribourg, 1910. Latest and fullest, but still leaving much to be desired despite its 252 pages, is A. Michelitsch, *Thomasschriften,* 1913, vol. I; which gives the sources for Aquinas' biography

Whether we believe that he was born in 1225 or 1227, he was not yet fifty when he died on the seventh of March, 1274. Ptolemy of Lucca, who states that he had often heard Aquinas' confession and had attended his lectures and been his friend for a long time,[1] says that Thomas became a Dominican at sixteen and "lived in pure innocence" for about thirty-two years thereafter.[2] A passage in the *Compendium studii philosophiae* of Roger Bacon sneers at the theological teaching of "the boys of the two Orders, such as Albert and Thomas and the others who enter the Orders when twenty

but too briefly with arbitrary omissions, the bare numbers of MSS containing his works without indication of their date or contents, the old lists of his writings, and a full analysis of the printed editions. Fossi (1793-1795) II, 663-98, lists such of Aquinas' works printed before 1500 as are in the Magliabechian library at Florence.

Since the edition of the works of Aquinas begun by order of Pope Leo XIII at Rome, 1886-1906, has never been completed, the most useful edition and that which I have employed remains that by E. Fretté and P. Maré, *Opera omnia*, Paris, 1871-1880, in 34 volumes.

I have not been much impressed by the worth of such secondary works on Aquinas and his science as I have happened upon: for some bibliography see Paetow (1917), pp. 406, 408-9. Paetow does not mention A. Farges, *Études philosophiques pour vulgariser les théories d'Aristote et de S. Thomas et montrer leur accord avec les sciences*, 1909; A. Fisichella, *S. Tommaso d'Aquino, Leone XIII e la scienza*, 1880; T. Gaudenzi, *S. Tommaso d'Aquino e la scienza*, 1874; Frohschammer, *Die Philosophie des Thomas von Aquino*, Leipzig, 1889; nor G. M. Cornoldi (1822-1892), *The Physical System of St. Thomas*, English translation by E. H. Dering, London, 1893. The last is a Roman Catholic defense of the natural philosophy of

Aquinas against modern science, which obscures the facts that Thomas held fast to the theory of four elements and derived his natural philosophy from Aristotle. Overworked as the words "camouflage" and "propaganda" are, one is tempted to apply them in the case of recent Aquinas literature. At the same time it is remarkable how few libraries have a complete and unexpurgated edition of his works. I have not seen F. Tessen-Wesierski, *Die Grundlagen des Wunderbegriffes nach Thomas von Aquino*, 1899, in *Jahrb. f. Philos. u. Spekulative Theologie.*

The relation of Aquinas to Dante has been the theme of more than one work; an example is N. Busetto, *Saggi di varia Psicologia Dantesca contribute allo studio delle relazioni di Dante con Alberto Magno e con San Tommaso*, 1905.

[1] Ptolemy of Lucca, *Hist. Eccles.*, XXIII, 7 (*Muratori*, XI, 1169), recounting the death of Aquinas remarks, "Unde cum multa devotione et mentis puritate et corporis qua semper floruit et in Ordine viguit, quemque ego probavi inter homines quos umquam novi qui suam saepe confessionem audivi et cum ipso multo tempore conversatus sum familiari ministerio ac ipsius auditor fui, ex hac luce transiit ad Christum. . . ."

[2] *Ibid.*, XXII, 20 (*Muratori*, XI, 1152).

years or under.[1] Perhaps the names of Albert and Thomas
were not in the passage as originally penned by Bacon; Albert at least had probably come of age before the friar orders
started, and Bacon would scarcely look back upon a man
who was his senior as a boy. But the fact remains that
Thomas at least became a Dominican at an early age.

Thomas of Cantimpré tells [2] how Aquinas entered the
Dominican order at Bologna against the wishes of his family—he was the son of the count of Aquino and the countess
of Teano—who secured a summons to the papal court where
he was ordered to put off the friar's dress and be invested
with ecclesiastical office. When he refused, his two brothers
secretly seized him and shut him up in prison where he suf-
fered from want, cold, and poverty, and further from
women whom his brothers introduced to tempt him. He remained thus imprisoned "for two or three years" according
to Thomas of Cantimpré, until master John of the Dominicans complained to the emperor Frederick II who secured Aquinas' release and would, according to Thomas
of Cantimpré, have put his brothers to death for
their inhumanity but for master John's further intervention.
Master John then shipped Aquinas off to Paris, but his
brothers and friends at the papal court had him again summoned thither, and he was offered the post of abbot of Monte
Cassino "under whom are seven bishops and who himself
exercises the pontifical office." The pope was ready to allow
him to continue to wear the Dominican costume in this position, but Aquinas fled a second time from the papal court
and came to Cologne and studied there until Albert was trans-
ferred to Paris and given the chair of theology there for his
incomparable learning. "After whom," continues Cantimpré, "also this same brother Thomas gained a position and
chair of similar importance." The meaning of this last sen-
tence is somewhat doubtful. Is "after" used in the sense of
time or of precedence in dignity? Did Aquinas hold a posi-

Early life according to Thomas of Can- timpré.

---

[1] Brewer (1859), p. 426.
[2] *Bonum universale de apibus*, I, 20, xi.

tion at the same time with and second only to Albert, or did he obtain the chair only after Albert had ceased to hold it? Chronological considerations make the latter more probable. But was the chair in question at Cologne or at Paris?

Is Thomas of Cantimpré's account reliable?

This passage from Thomas of Cantimpré is at variance on a number of points with the accounts usually given of Aquinas' life. For instance, it makes him join the Dominicans at Bologna, not at Naples, and represents the pope as siding with his family in their efforts to keep Aquinas out of the Dominican Order instead of delivering Aquinas from the persecution of his family. But Thomas of Cantimpré apparently penned his passage during Aquinas' lifetime and it is probably a half century nearer the events than the *Lives* of Aquinas written in the early fourteenth century and upon which most modern accounts are based. At the same time it must be admitted that Cantimpré seems to write in a loose and exaggerated manner which does not command much confidence. But I suspect that he is the ultimate source of most of the later accounts covering the same ground.

Ptolemy of Lucca on his early life.

Ptolemy of Lucca, who may be regarded as an independent witness in view of his personal friendship with Aquinas, states that Thomas was of noble origin and descended from great counts of the kingdom of Apulia, that his family were faithful to the pope against the emperor Frederick II, and that Thomas was educated as a boy in the monastery of Monte Cassino. When he joined the Dominicans at sixteen, his relations kidnapped him, but he escaped to Rome and from there went off to Cologne to become Albert's pupil. At the age of twenty-five he came to Paris where before his thirtieth year he lectured on the *Sentences* and received his degree in theology. Before receiving the degree he had written a commentary on the *Sentences* and a treatise against William of St. Amour. As William of St. Amour was not condemned by the pope until October, 1256, and as the friars were not admitted to the doctorate in theology at Paris until 1257 or 1258, Ptolemy's statements would indicate that Thomas was not born until 1227.

On the other hand, the assertions of both Cantimpré and Ptolemy of Lucca that Aquinas studied with Albert at Cologne before Albert was called to Paris, do not fit in any too well with the usual dating of Albert's Paris residence as from 1245 to 1248, when he is again supposed to have returned to Cologne. Consequently Peter of Prussia in his fifteenth century life of Albertus Magnus held that Aquinas spent two periods of study with Albert at Cologne, one before and the other after Albert's teaching at Paris.[1] Similarly von Hertling[2] gives 1245-1252 as the duration of Aquinas' studies with Albert, after which he returned to Paris alone.

Only sixteen or seventeen years of life remained to Aquinas after he received his degree in theology. Ptolemy of Lucca states that he remained in Paris for only three years after receiving the degree, when he returned to Italy, where during the pontificates of Urban IV (1261-1264) and Clement IV (1265-1268) he resided at Viterbo, Orvieto, and Rome, and was offered but declined the archbishopric of Naples. During these same years Ptolemy places most of his chief works. In 1268 or 1269 he returned to Paris, but died in Italy in 1274.

Aquinas rapidly attained great success as a teacher and authority as a theologian during his lifetime and seems still to be regarded as the greatest and most authoritative of the orthodox medieval theologians. This success was probably due to the fact that he did just a little better than anyone else what a great many had been and were trying to do, and that was to combine all previous Christian thinking into one systematic and consistent and moderate whole. Aquinas was probably not the most brilliant or original mind of his generation, but probably his teaching and writing were clearer to a greater number of students, and seemed sounder to a

Marginal notes: Date and place of his studies with Albert. His closing years. His success as a theologian.

[1] Peter of Prussia (1621), pp. 90-104.
[2] v. Hertling (1914), p. 9, note, where, however, he says, "Albert's Lehrtätigkeit an der Universität Paris schloss sich unmittelbar an jene von Strassburg," which leaves no time for Aquinas to come to Albert in the first instance at Cologne.

greater number of the thinkers of the time than the lectures or books of any other contemporary. He put matters clearly, concisely, moderately, and convincingly; and struck the golden mean as it were. We can see how he may have profited immensely by the work of predecessors like William of Auvergne and Albertus Magnus, and yet how his works would tend to supplant theirs. Moreover, the task at which he had been working was not one which admitted of infinite improvement. It was largely a problem of combining, classifying, reconciling, and presenting the views of previous generations and periods, and when this was once well done, there was no need of doing it again. The attitude therefore of Aquinas toward magic and witchcraft, astrology and divination, and other occult arts and sciences, and also toward natural science is quite important for us to note, since he summed up previous Christian thought so satisfactorily, since he was both the most popular and the most moderate teacher of his own time, and since his opinions upon these subjects remained for centuries acceptable and authoritative to the Roman Catholic Church.[1] At the same time for these very reasons we must not expect to find him putting forward any new and unusual views upon these points.

His commentaries on Aristotle.

Aquinas was not merely a theologian in a narrow and restricted sense of that word, but was also noted as a commentator on Aristotle.[2] Ptolemy of Lucca tells us that "he expounded practically all philosophy, whether moral or natural, but especially ethics and mathematics." These lectures, however, were not all published. Thomas did not comment on as many of the Aristotelian works as Albert did, and several of his commentaries were left unfinished and

[1] Some measure of Aquinas' hold upon the later middle ages may be had from the list of his works printed before 1500 and contained in the Magliabechian library at Florence: F. Fossi, *Catalogus codicum saeculo XV impressorum qui in publica Bibliotheca Magliabechiana Florentiae adservantur*, 1793-1795, II, 663-98.

[2] I have not had access to M. Grabmann, *Les Commentaires de Saint Thomas d'Aquin sur les ouvrages d'Aristote*, in *Annales de l'Institut Supérieur de Philosophie*, Louvain, III (1914), 229-82, nor to R. Simiterre, *Sur les condemnations d'Aristote et de Saint Thomas d'Aquin au XIIIe siècle*, in *Revue pratique d'Apologétique*, V (1907), 502-15.

were completed by others such as Peter of Auvergne. Thomas has sometimes been given credit for bringing about and using as the basis of his commentaries a new translation of Aristotle, made directly from the Greek and presumably executed by William of Moerbeke,[1] although, as we have already noted in the case of Peter of Prussia's *Life of Albertus Magnus,* some say by Thomas of Cantimpré. It is true that William of Moerbeke translated some of the works of Aristotle, but I cannot find that anyone has ever identified a signed translation by him with the text used by Aquinas or otherwise adequately demonstrated that they worked in concert.[2] Even if Aquinas instigated William's translations

[1] Thus Rashdall, *The Universities of Europe in the Middle Ages,* 1895, I, 361, says, "Thomas Aquinas endeavored to procure better translations from the original Greek, and his efforts were seconded by Pope Urban IV. Special translations or special revisions of the existing Graeco-Latin translations were prepared for his use by a Dominican Friar of Greek birth, variously known as Wilhelmus de Brabantia or Wilhelmus de Moerbeka. To him at least the common tradition of the Middle Ages ascribes the *translatio nova* of the books of Natural and Moral Philosophy, which, in spite of many imperfections, held its place in the schools as a kind of authorized version of Aristotle till the dawn of the New Learning." Citing Jourdain, *Recherches,* p. 67, *et seq.;* Denifle, *Archiv,* II, 226-7. William the Fleming, as he is also called, was scarcely of Greek birth, but of course finally became archbishop of Corinth.

[2] In the 14th century bibliography of writings by Dominicans, Denifle (1886), p. 237, it is stated that William of Brabant, archbishop of Corinth (he became so in 1277 after Aquinas' death), "translated all the books of natural and moral philosophy from Greek into Latin at the instance of brother Thomas." But of the numerous signed translations by

William extant very few are of works by Aristotle. Moreover, is the Thomas here mentioned Aquinas? The very next name in the bibliography in question to follow this Wilhelmus Brabantinus is Thomas Brabantinus or Thomas of Cantimpré, who may have been the person to suggest the translation to his fellow Fleming. However, Aquinas and William were both connected with the popes in Italy in the 1260's, and Aquinas would seem to have had more interest in a translation of Aristotle than Albert's other "auditor," Thomas of Cantimpré.

The following extracts from medieval chronicles specifically mention Aquinas, but as their dates are obviously incorrect not much reliance is to be placed upon them.

In Chronico Slavicorum apud Lindenbrogium ad annum 1249. "Wilhelmus de Brabantia Ordinis Praedicatorum transtulit omnes libros Aristotelis de graeco in Latinum verbum a verbo (qua translatione scholares adhuc hodierna die utuntur in scholis) ad instantiam sancti Thomae de Aquino Doctoris."

In Chronico Susati, quod MS servat Veneta SS. Ioannis et Pauli bibliotheca. "Anno Domini 1267 fr. Wilhelmus Brabantinus, corinthiensis de Ordine fratrum Praedicatorum, rebus excessit humanis, baccalarius in theologia. Hic

from Aristotle, he could not have taken full advantage of them, since some of William's work of translation was executed after Aquinas' death.[1]

The spheres of theology and science. We must not think of Aquinas' studies in secular philosophy and science as simply aimed to render these subjects serviceable and innocuous to Christian theology. He was too much a student of Albertus Magnus for that, and his study of Greek thought and natural science broadened his outlook beyond that of theology in a narrow sense. He believed, moreover, that to a large extent the fields of theology and natural science were distinct; that pure theologians should not try to settle purely philosophical or scientific problems, of which they knew little. Christians who deny as contrary to their faith the philosophical solutions of problems which are really indifferent so far as the Faith is concerned, simply bring Christianity, in Aquinas' opinion, into disrepute among the wise men of this world.[2] Conversely every theory of an ancient philosopher or hypothesis of science is not to be accepted as of equal rank with religious dogmas.   When

transtulit omnes libros Aristotelis Rationalis Naturalis et Moralis Philosophiae et Metaphysicae de graeco in latinum, verbum a verbo, quibus nunc utimur in scholis ad instantiam sancti Thomae de Aquino. Nam temporibus domini Alberti translatione vetere omnes communiter utebantur." "Albert's day" was of course no different from Aquinas' whom he outlived by six years.

In 1847 the *Histoire Littéraire,* XXI, 147, said, "Guillaume de Meerbeke passe pour avoir traduit tous les livres d'Aristote, à la prière de saint Thomas. Nous n'oserions affirmer ni cette intervention du docteur angélique, ni cette immensité des travaux du traducteur brabançon. Il s'en faut qu'on ait de lui une série si volumineuse de versions latines."

[1] As has been pointed out by HL XXI, 147, in the case of the "new translation" of the Ethics, dated in the colophon in 1282, whereas Aquinas died in 1274. Quetif and

Echard (1719), I, 390, had argued, however, that this date was when the MS was copied and not when the translation was made; but this is far-fetched as most of William's translations are similarly dated. Certainly William's labors as a translator did not cease with his elevation to the archbishopric of Corinth, since he translated Galen *De alimentis* in 1277 and works by Proclus in 1281.

Quetif and Echard, in order to maintain the cooperation supposed to exist between William and Aquinas, also hold that William's translation of the *Elementatio theologica* of Proclus made at Viterbo in 1268 was from the Arabic and not from the Greek, since Aquinas says in his commentary on that work that the Greek text had not yet been found.   This conclusion is also drawn by HL XXI, 148.

[2] See Duhem II (1914), 394, for a like opinion expressed by Augustine.

John of Vercelli submitted a list of questions upon which he desired, first, the opinions of the saints, and secondly, the opinion of Aquinas himself, Thomas protested at the start that some of the inquiries had nothing to do with the Christian faith but were purely physical.[1]

Furthermore we must keep in mind that Aquinas was something of a scientist himself. It is interesting to note that after his death the University of Paris wrote to the general chapter of the Dominicans, not only lamenting his death as an irreparable loss and asking that his bones might be sent to Paris for burial, but also requesting the transmission of certain books begun by him while at the university and not as yet completed upon his departure from Paris.[2] What were these writings: theological treatises, commentaries on the minor prophets, or manuals of devotion? None of these. They were a commentary on the philosopher Simplicius, another on the *De coelo et mundo* of Aristotle,[3] a third on the *Timaeus* of Plato, and finally a work on irrigation and mechanical engineering.[4]

Aquinas as a scientist.

Thomas, however, did no such important work in natural science as Albert. His commentaries upon Aristotle follow the text closely and do little more than expound it; they are not full of long digressions and additions, as Albert's are.

Inferior to Albert.

[1] *Opera*, 27, 248.
[2] *Chartularium univ. Paris.* (1889-1891), I, 504-5, dated May 2, 1274, ". . . humiliter supplicamus ut cum quaedam scripta ad phylosophiam spectantia, Parisius inchoata ab eo, quae in suo recessu reliquerit imperfecta, et ipsum credamus, ubi translatus fuerit, complevisse, nobis benevolentia vestra cito communicari procuret, et specialiter super librum Simplicii, super librum de celo et mundo; et expositionem Tymei Platonis, ac librum de aquarum conductibus et ingeniis erigendis; de quibus nobis mittendis speciali promissione fecerat mentionem."
[3] Of this commentary the third and fourth books were finished by Peter of Auvergne.

[4] Aquinas is even credited with an abridgement of the Almagest in CLM 56, 1436 A. D., "Almagesti abbreviatum per magistrum Thomam de Aquino"; cited by Björnbo (1911), p. 129. But this, I take it, is the same as the abridgement of the Almagest which Averroes is said to have made and which was translated by the order of Alfonso the Great: see Digby 236, 14th century, fol. 190, where the writer of a prologue to another work of Averroes remarks, "Scivit enim Averoys optime Almagestum. Nam vidi per eum Almagesti abbreviatum, quem librum fecit transferri Rex Alfonsus Magnus, et habetur Bononie et in Hispania."

TOWNSHIP PUBLIC LIBRARY

Thomas did not found an experimental school and had not himself devoted the long years of personal experience and observation to nature that his master had. And he seems to have had the less original and observant mind of the two. But his wide reading, his clear thinking, his well-ordered class-room presentation of material and arguments, and his broad yet moderate views insured his instant and permanent success in the field of theology, where the paths were already well trod, and it only remained for someone to put everything into as perfect and final a form as possible. In natural science, on the other hand, the labor that awaited men was not merely the lucid combination of Aristotelian and Arabic thinking with previous Christian thought, but the pioneer work of personal observation and experiment and the far more difficult combination of these with existing theories. Aquinas was a perfecter according to the standards of his own age; Albert sometimes was a pioneer in the spirit of the new age of science.

Aquinas' theological approach to the subject of magic.

In view of this distinction between the two men it is perhaps not surprising that what Aquinas has to say concerning magic, even in the broad use of that term, occurs to a large extent in his theological writings. Just as, although Albert was a distinguished theologian, we viewed magic in his works largely as connected with science; so, although Aquinas studied and wrote of secular philosophy and science, we find in him a moderate, enlightened, and highly influential statement of the attitude of Christian theological scholarship towards magic, witchcraft, and astrology. In his account of magic so-called in his *Summa, Contra Gentiles,* and *De potentia,* he seems to follow Augustine a good deal, and like him he makes considerable use of Porphyry's *Letter to Anebo.* Aquinas accepts the essential features of the previous theological definition of magic, as Albert did in his *theological* treatises.

Aquinas carefully distinguishes magic from miracle.[1]   A

[1] *Summa,* Prima pars, Quaest. 110, Art. 4, and Quaest. 111, Art. 3; *Contra Gentiles,* III, 101-3; *De potentia,* VI, 5; *Sententiae,* II, Dist. 7, Quaest. 2-3.

miracle is contrary to the order of all created nature and can be performed by God alone. Many things that seem marvelous to us or of which the cause is hidden from us are not, strictly speaking, miraculous. An eclipse seems a miracle to some ignorant people, but not to a philosopher who understands its cause. Other seeming marvels which are not divine miracles are the occult virtues of physical bodies "for which a reason cannot be assigned by man," [1] and the effects produced in our lower world by the influence of the constellations. Even more difficult of human comprehension are the doings of demons, who, Aquinas is convinced, can not only deceive the senses and affect the human imagination, but also truly transform bodies. Yet even their feats are not true miracles in violation of natural order; they simply add to the marvelous virtues of physical objects and the potent influences of the stars something of their own peculiar powers. After all, their feats can be explained, they operate by means of art; God alone is a cause absolutely hidden from every man.

Miracle distinguished.

As for magicians, in their feats they make use of herbs and other physical bodies; of words, usually in the form of "invocations, supplications, and adjurations"; they also employ figures and characters, sacrifices and prostrations, images and rites, carefully observed times, constellations, and other considerations.[2] As a result the whereabouts of stolen objects is disclosed, hidden treasure is found, the future is revealed, closed doors mysteriously open, men become invisible, inanimate bodies move and speak, apparitions of rational beings are summoned and answer questions. Some contend that such apparitions are imaginary, but Aquinas replies that on such occasions third parties have been present whose senses were working normally and who also witnessed the apparitions, and furthermore that no phantom of our imagination could reveal things of which we

Reality of magic affirmed.

---

[1] *Summa,* Secundae secunda, Quaest. 96, Art. 2.
[2] *Contra Gentiles,* III, 101-5;

De potentia, VI, 10; *Summa,* Prima pars, Quaest. 115, Art. 5; *De substantiis separatis,* cap. 2.

ourselves were ignorant. In the reality of such feats of magic, then, Thomas firmly believes.

Magic not a science but due to demons.

But Aquinas will not admit that the magician and his materials are a sufficient cause of the magic. He also denies that certain men are especially endowed with magic power by the stars at their birth or that the influence of the constellations can be controlled to perform particular feats of magic. Demons in his opinion really perform the magic. Words, figures, spells are mere signs to them; the poor magician is their dupe. It looks, Thomas admits, as if spirits came only when invoked, and as if they often came unwillingly, and sometimes performed good deeds at the magician's bidding which must be very distasteful to them as evil beings. But in all this they are simply deceiving mankind. "It is not true then," says Aquinas, "that the magic arts are sciences, but rather they are certain fallacies of the demons." [1] In discussing the "notory art," which professes to acquire knowledge by fasting, prayers to God, figures, and strange words, he declares that demons cannot illuminate the intellect, although they may express in words some smattering of the sciences.[2]

And is evil.

Aquinas further charges that the practitioners of magic are generally criminals, perpetrating illicit deeds, adulteries, thefts, and homicides, a fact which has gained for magicians the further name of evil-doers, i. e. *malefici* (sorcerers). At best magic does not aid man in science or virtue, but in trivial matters such as the discovery of stolen goods.[3] Aquinas repeats the criticism of Porphyry in *The Letter to Anebo* that the methods of magic are immoral. Therefore it is wrong to seek to learn "the magic sciences" in order to use them, but permissible to study them in order to confute them. Aquinas then makes haste to correct this phrase "magic sciences," as we have already noted above.

Some regard magic as a human art or science.

But by his own denial Aquinas makes it sufficiently evident that many men of his time thought the magic arts

[1] *Quodlibet,* IV, 16.
[2] *Summa,* Secundae secunda,
Quest. 96, Art. 1.
[3] *Contra Gentiles,* III, 106.

sciences, and that magicians believed themselves able by personal qualifications, by subtle use of occult natural properties, by rites and ceremonies, and by the art of astrology, either to work wonders directly and immediately or to coerce demons to work wonders for them.

In lending the authority of his name to an affirmation of the reality of demon-magic, Aquinas must share together with many writers before and after him responsibility for the witchcraft delusion and executions. And yet he tells us that there were already some persons by his time who denied that there was any such thing as witchcraft except in men's imaginations and fears. Such persons argued that where the supposed sorcery was not entirely due to imaginary terror, it could be explained as the natural effect of occult causes. But Aquinas, who twice argues the question whether the consummation of marriage can be prevented by sorcery,[1] declares that the authority of the saints and of the Catholic faith alike proclaim the reality of witchcraft and its power to obstruct carnal union. Men who dispute this are the same as denying the existence of the demons.[2] Dear demons! What a treasured legacy of theology from paganism!

Aquinas believes in witchcraft.

Aquinas also tends to follow ecclesiastical tradition in condemning most arts of divination as the work of demons,[3] and in carefully distinguishing from them divine prophecy, which can speak with certainty even of contingent matters.[4] He grants, however, that some arts of divination have a natural basis, and that natural divination is permissible, if not extended to accidental occurrences and to human acts due to the reason and will.[5] It is possible to forecast the future by interpretation of dreams which are produced by natural causes either within or outside the sleeper's body.[6] The commentary of Aquinas on Aristotle's *De somno et vigilia* is,

Divination.

---

[1] For the opinions of Hincmar, Gratian, Peter Lombard, and other ecclesiastical authorities on this question of witchcraft and impotency see Hansen (1900), p. 153.

[2] *Quodlibet*, XI, 10; *Comment.*

in Lib. IV Sententiarum, Dist. 34, Art. 3.

[3] *In Isaiam*, cap. 3; *Summa*, II, ii, 95; *De sortibus, passim*.

[4] *Contra Gentiles*, III, 154.

[5] *Summa*, II, ii, 95, art. 5.

[6] *Ibid.*, art. 6.

however, a perfunctory treatise, inferior to that by Albertus Magnus on the same theme, and advances no ideas of Thomas' own on the subject of divination from dreams. Even augury may be natural divination, if the acts of the animals under observation are governed by the positions and movements of the stars.[1] Aquinas also mentions chiromancy without disapproval, but will not admit that geomancy comes under the head of natural divination, since the figures upon which its predictions are based are the outcome either of chance or of voluntary human action.[2] He condemns as superstitious the regarding as signs of the future such trivial occurrences as a sneeze or a dog's running between two persons who are walking together.[3]

Lot casting.

Lot casting of whatever sort is not natural divination. The Bible tells us, however, that God often rules the casting of lots, and "if practices which have a natural or human cause are blameless, much more so are those which depend on divine aid."[4] But Aquinas cautions against an appeal to God to decide the casting of lots unless there is real necessity, or without due reverence and devotion, or for purely human and worldly purposes, or in cases where direct divine inspiration should be sought, as in ecclesiastical elections. As Bede pointed out, it is true that Matthias was selected by lot before Pentecost, but after the reception of the Holy Ghost the seven deacons were elected by the disciples. And when men pry into hidden things more than they should, whether by lot casting or other methods, it is Aquinas' opinion that demons are involved.[5]

[1] *Summa*, II, ii, 95, art. 7.
[2] *De sortibus,* caps. 3-4.
[3] *Summa,* II, ii, 95, art. 8, and 96.
[4] For the *Lots of the Saints* or *Apostles* see: CLM 14846, 10th century, fols. 106-21, "Sortilegia per literas et sacros libros quorum meminit Gregorius Turonensis" (see *Historia Francorum,* IV, 16); Egerton 821, fols. 54v-56r; BN nouv. acq. 4227, 13th century, in Provençal (consult Felix Rocquain, *Bibl. d. l'École des Chartes,*

1880, pp. 457-74; ed. by C. Chabaneau, with Latin original, Montpellier, 1881, and *Revue des langues romanes,* XVIII-XIX); Vienna 2155, 14th century, fols. 54-56, *Sortes apostolorum.*
[5] Aquinas' discussion occurs in his *De sortibus,* caps. 4-5. This treatise, which he wrote for the duchess of Brabant, is apt to precede or follow his equally brief *De occultis operibus* in the MSS: as in Corpus Christi 225, 14th century, fol. 232; Brussels (Li-

As Aquinas differentiated between natural divination and that due to demons, so he distinguishes from illicit magic "the occult works of nature." On this theme he addressed a brief treatise to "a certain knight." [1] Besides those properties of natural objects which accord with the properties of their component elements and so have a manifest origin, there are occult virtues for which men can give no reason,[2] as in the stock illustration of the magnet, as great a favorite with medieval writers as electricity is with modern preachers to inspire faith in the invisible and imperfectly known. Aquinas accounts for the existence of such occult virtues by the influence of the heavenly bodies upon the world of nature. In his *Meteorology,* too, he attributes the wonderful powers of precious stones to "a certain celestial and occult virtue." [3] In this he probably shows the influence of his master Albertus Magnus.

Occult virtues

Aquinas declares that alchemy is a true, although difficult art, and accounts for the efficacy of its operations by its utilization of occult forces of celestial virtue.[4] Pico della Mirandola noted that while Thomas seemed to deny the art in his *Commentary on the Sentences,* he approved it in his theological *Summa,* which Pico accepted as his last word on

Alchemy and fascination.

brary of Dukes of Burgundy) 2471, 15th century; CLM 3754, 14-15th century, fol. 51.

In Bologna University Library 1158, fols. 49v-52v, is a different *De Sortibus* from that of Aquinas. It has six or seven sections: the first inquiring what lots are; the second whether they are good or bad, permitted or prohibited; third, if prohibited, when, and if not always, why not; fourth, whether to cast lots is to tempt God; fifth, whether they were permissible before Christ but not since; sixth, why women are often better at lot-casting than men. The last question, which appears to have been whether the subjects of lot casting could be evil, seems to be left unfinished.

[1] *Opera,* 27, 504-7, *De occultis operibus naturae ad quemdam militem.* Other forms of the title found in the MSS are, *De actionibus occultis naturae, De occultis actionibus rerum,* and *De operationibus occultis.* MSS are numerous: for instance, at Paris alone, BN 3899, 6738A, 6786, 16195; an anonymous *De operibus occultis* in BN 16096, 13th century, fols. 120v-122r, I find on examination to be that of Aquinas. MSS of it at Munich are: CLM 402, 3754, 6942.

[2] *Summa,* II, ii, 96, art. 2, "Res autem naturales habent quasdam virtutes occultas quarum ratio ab homine assignari non potest."

[3] *Meteor.,* III, 9.

[4] *Ibid.,* "Unde etiam ipsi Alchimistae per veram artem alchimiae sed tamen difficilem, propter occultas operationes virtutis coelestis. . . ."

the subject.[1] Spurious works of alchemy were, however, subsequently ascribed to Aquinas in manuscripts of the fifteenth century. Fascination Aquinas also regards as a fact, and practically explains it as due to the power of the evil eye. The eye is affected by the strong imagination of the soul and then corrupts and poisons the atmosphere so that tender bodies coming within its range may be injuriously affected. It is thus that malicious old women injure children,[2]—another faggot added by Aquinas to the pyres of the witchcraft delusion.

Amulets and incantations.   We have hitherto found the practices of wearing amulets and repeating incantations apt to accompany the belief in occult virtues. Aquinas, in discussing "the suspension of sacred words about the neck" cautions that "in all incantations and suspensions of writings" what is written should be seemly, should not be an invocation of demons, should contain no unknown words which may have an evil meaning, and should contain no characters other than the sign of the cross. He quotes the decretal forbidding other observances in collecting medicinal herbs than the sign of the cross and repetition of the Lord's prayer. And he concludes that "suspending divine words about the neck, assuming that they contain nothing false or doubtful, is certainly permissible, but it would be more laudable to abstain from such practices."[3]

Attitude to astrology.   Already a number of passages have shown incidentally that Thomas, like his master Albert, ascribed an important place in natural science to astrological theory. Although he refused to explain magic as worked by the stars, he accounted for the occult works of nature and for natural divination by astral influence. He grants the nobility and incorruptibility of the heavenly bodies but, although aware that Plato and Aristotle attributed souls and intelligences to them, insists that they are material substances. But he regards the stars as

---

[1] *Pico della Mirandola* (1586), II, 6, p. 51.

[2] *Contra Gentiles,* III, 103; *Sum-* ma, I, 117, 3.

[3] *Summa,* II, ii, 96, art. 4.

media between "the separate intelligences" and our material world and is inclined to answer affirmatively a question which was more than once put to him, namely, Do the angels move the stars?[1] He also frequently affirms, both in the course of his chief works and in briefer answers to special inquiries that God rules inferior through superior creatures and earthly bodies by the stars.[2] No wise man doubts that all natural motions of inferior bodies are caused by the movement of the celestial bodies.[3] Reason and experience, saints and philosophers, have proved it over and over again. Aquinas then cites two passages from Augustine [4] and Dionysius [5] which do not seem so sweeping as his own assertion: Augustine affirming merely that "grosser and inferior bodies are ruled by subtler and superior ones according to a certain order," and Dionysius saying simply that the rays of the sun aid in the generation of life and nourish and increase and perfect it. Indeed, throughout his arguments for astrology Aquinas, like Albert, seems to stretch authorities upon a Procrustean bed of citation and to make church fathers who are famed for their attacks on astrologers seem to favor the limited rule of the stars over all nature. Aquinas further deems an art of judicial astrology possible, asserting that, besides the crude prognostications which sailors and farmers make from the sky, it is feasible "by some other more occult observations of the stars to employ judicial astrology concerning corporeal effects."[6]

But Aquinas declares that the human will is free and that the soul as an intellectual substance cannot be coerced by

[1] *Responsio ad Magistrum Joannem de Vercellis. Responsio ad lectorem Venetum*, Artic. 1-2. *De substantiis separatis.*, cap. 1 (*Opera*, 27, 275), "Ipsae etiam animae coelestium corporum si tamen sint animata, inter Angelos sint connumerandae, ut Augustinus definit in *Enchyridione*."

[2] Besides the treatises mentioned in the preceding note, see the *Summa, Tractatus de fide, Meteorologicorum libri IV, De judiciis astrorum ad fratrem Reginaldum*, Commentary on Matthew.

[3] *Opera*, 27, 249, *Ad J. de Vercellis*.

[4] *De trinitate*, III.

[5] *De divinis nominibus*, IV.

[6] *De judiciis astrorum, Opera* 27, 449. MSS of this treatise, too, are numerous: for instance, at Paris BN 6786, 3109, 3899, 6512, 15690; and at Munich CLM 402, 5594, 27001, 3754, 6942.

Extent of and limits to the influence of the stars upon man. corporeal substances, however superior. He also opines that many occurrences are accidental rather than due to the stars, "as when a man digging a grave finds buried treasure." [1] And "no natural agent can incline one to that which happens accidentally." Aquinas like Albert is also aware, however, that the astrologers themselves agree that the wise man rules the stars, and conversely he himself recognizes that man is not purely an intellectual being, that he often obeys sensual appetite, and that even the mind derives its knowledge from the senses and consequently in a condition disturbed by phantasy. Thus the stars may indirectly affect the human intellect to a considerable extent. [2] Aquinas is also ready to admit that astrologers often make true predictions in events where large numbers of men are concerned and the passions of the majority override the wisdom and will of the few who are able to resist such impulses. On the other hand, he holds that astrologers often err in their predictions concerning individuals. [3] This perhaps refers only to prediction of nativities, for Peter of Prussia, in defending Albertus Magnus against the charge of indulgence in too curious arts, asserted that Aquinas "nowhere in his writings" reproved or attacked astrological interrogations. [4]

Power of astrological images denied. The question remains, to what extent can men voluntarily avail themselves of the celestial virtues? Aquinas takes the position that men can make use of such virtues only as they find them already existing in nature and that works of human art, as distinct from natural objects, receive no new virtue from the stars but only from the human operator,— "from the conception of the artificer." It is for this reason that Aquinas refuses to explain many operations of magicians as produced by the aid of the constellations. In particular he denies that gems engraved with astronomical figures receive any more virtue from the stars than other gems of the same species without the carving. Figures and characters and human words are immaterial and do not exert

[1] *De sortibus*, cap. 4.
[2] *Summa* I, 115, 4. *De fide*, cap. 129.
[3] *Ibid.*, and *De sortibus*, cap. 4.
[4] Peter of Prussia (1621), cap. 15.

force upon matter. If, therefore, astronomical or necromantic or magic images and characters seem to produce marvelous effects, it must be because they are illicitly employed as secret signs to demons who really achieve the results.[1] In short, Aquinas' position concerning images and characters is that of William of Auvergne rather than that of Albertus Magnus.

Aquinas discusses the problem of the star of Bethlehem both in his *Commentary on Matthew*[2] and in the *Summa*,[3] and the interest which such subjects had for his contemporaries is further shown by these questions which were put to him, "Did the little hands of the infant Jesus create stars?" and "Did the star which appeared to the Magi have the shape of a cross or human form?"[4] The first question was probably suggested by the apocryphal gospels, the second by the homily of the Pseudo-Chrysostom which we have already considered. Aquinas' discussion of the star and Magi is somewhat fuller than that by Abelard but equally drawn from the fathers, especially Chrysostom and Augustine.[5]

The Magi and the star.

[1] *Contra Gentiles,* III, 105; *Summa,* II, ii, 96, *artic.* 2; *De occultis operibus.*

[2] *Comment. in Math.,* cap. 2.

[3] *Summa,* III, 36.

[4] *Responsio de vi articulis ad lectorem Bisuntinum.*

[5] As we have already been over their arguments, Aquinas' presentation thereof may perhaps be better summarized here than in the text. The Gospel account led the Priscillianists to subject all human acts to fate and the Manicheans to repudiate the Book of Matthew as inculcating a belief in fate. Against them are rehearsed the following arguments. First, as Augustine says (*Contra Faustum,* II, 5), no astrologer asserts that a star will leave its usual position at a man's birth and go to him, as the Gospel narrative asserts that the star in the east did, and hence Matthew confounds rather than defends the error of astrology. Aquinas then quotes with apparent approval the erroneous assertion of Chrysostom (*Homily 6 in Matth.*) that "it is not astronomy's task to tell from the stars who are being born, but to predict the future from the hour of nativity." He also notes Chrysostom's objection that it took the Magi over two years to travel to Bethlehem so that the star must have appeared two years before Christ's birth. This, by the way, would make the date 4 B. C., usually given for the birth of Christ, fit nicely into Münter's date of 6 B. C. for the constellation which portended it. Aquinas also repeats the argument that the star was probably a new creation of God.

But all these criticisms are really quite beside the point, since even according to the Bible story, the Magi, who were evidently astronomers, knew perfectly well what the star meant. Indeed, Aquinas himself repeats the statement that the birth of Christ was announced to them by

Like them he contends that the incident lends no support to the doctrine of nativities. He saves the Magi, however, from the imputation of being workers of magic and dupes of the demons, adopting Jerome's oft-repeated explanation that while in common speech *magi* are the same as enchanters. in the Persian language the word designates philosophers and sages. In this case Aquinas does not force his authorities at all; on the contrary he makes no attempt to improve upon their captious, sophistical, and unconvincing arguments.

Is the *De fato* spurious? The earliest bibliography of Aquinas' works seems to be that which Ptolemy of Lucca, who had known him personally, gives in his *Ecclesiastical History*.[1] Among the *Opuscula*, which Ptolemy lists with considerable care, giving their *Incipits* as well as their titles, appears the treatise *De fato*.[2] It also appears in the *Table of writings of the Order of Preachers*, a bibliography completed in the second quarter of the fourteenth century.[3] It is not, however, in the official list of Thomas' works drawn up preliminary to his canonization in 1323, and which Father Mandonnet would accept as an absolute criterion of the authentic writings of Aquinas. Other early catalogues of Aquinas' writings are all derived from one of these three prototypes.[4] Our treatise has also

a star, although to Simon and Anna and to the shepherds by other methods, because they were used to stars. If it was a very unusual kind of star and had a very unusual meaning, all that simply goes to show that a good astrologer is equal to any emergency. Aquinas, indeed, or rather, his authorities, sees the need of stating some other method than astrological skill by which the Magi comprehended the significance of the star. He adduces two explanations from Augustine (*Sermo 374 de Epiphania*, and *De quaest. vet. et nov. test.*, *Quaest. 63*); one that they were admonished by angels, which makes us wonder why there was any star at all; the other, that

Balaam had left them a prediction concerning the coming of the star.

Aquinas also repeats something of what the fathers have said on the allegorical significance of the Magi. But on the whole he, like his authorities, fails signally to explain away the astrological significance of the Magi.

[1] *Hist. eccles.* XXIII, 13 (Muratori XI, 1170). Michelitsch *Thomasschriften*, I (1913), p. 126, dates Ptolemy's list between 1312 and 1317, but I do not know why.

[2] It is included in Fretté and Maré, *Opera*, 27, 454-64.

[3] Denifle (1886), p. 237.

[4] Pierre Mandonnet, O. P. *Des Écrits Authentiques de S. Thomas d'Aquin*, Fribourg, 1910.

been attributed to Albertus Magnus,[1] and much of its attitude toward astrology and other occult arts is just the opposite of Thomas' position elsewhere as we have already noted it. I have therefore reserved the *De fato* for separate consideration. This problem of "fate" also sometimes formed the subject of a section of theological *Summae* or other long works, as we have seen in the case of Albertus Magnus, and the manuscripts contain other separate discussions of it [2] than this one associated with Aquinas. As might be expected there is a general resemblance between the aspects of the problem considered and the authorities cited in all these treatises. No doubt it was a common topic of scholastic disputation.

Fate is defined in our treatise as the power of the stars exercised through their movements and relations to one another. After citing in typical scholastic fashion a number of authorities *pro* and *con,*—Aristotle and Boethius are made to supply many arguments for astrology; and after agreeing with most of the favoring arguments and answering some of the opposing ones, the author finally concludes that fate in

Fate and the stars.

[1] See the list of writings ascribed to Albert in Borgnet's edition of his works, I, lxii. I have also seen the treatise ascribed to Albert in the Explicit of Sloane 2156, 15th century, fols. 154-9.

In Bologna University Library, 1158, 14th century, where the first treatise in the MS at fols. 1-39 is the treatise of Aquinas against William of St. Amour, our treatise together with another *De fato* which follows it and brief treatises on divination and lots are catalogued together as fols. 41-52, "Magistri Alberti theotonici de fato, de divinatione, de sortibus." In the MS itself, however, the only statements as to authorship are headings in the margin. That at the beginning of our *De fato* seems to be "Magri" (Magistri) "Alrti" (or Alxri, rather than Alberti) and a third word which looks like "Theotonici." The second *De fato* is headed "Magri (Magistri) Alexandri" in the up-

per margin of fol. 45r, and the next treatise is headed, fol. 47r, "Questio de divinatione Alexandri." The anonymous *De sortibus* which follows it is also not Aquinas'. The second treatise on fate considers six questions, of which the last is whether Christ was physically subject to the influence of the constellations like other men.

[2] In BN 16096, 13th century, fol. 138r-, is another which seems different from either of the *De fato's* mentioned in the preceding note. The catalogue questioningly assigns it to Alexander, but is probably misled by a rubric at fol. 139v which seems to be simply a citation ("in sic inscripto libro") and which reads, "Alexandri affridisei ad imperatores antoninum et severinum liber de fato." In this same MS at fols. 120v-122r occurs Aquinas' *De occultis operibus.*

this sense does prevail. But he distinguishes between fate and fatal necessity, holding that the stars do not impose fatal necessity upon inferiors. While their own motion is "necessary, inevitable, and inalterable, . . . in things generated it is received mutably and contingently because of their changeable natures." Like Aquinas and other authors, he then approvingly quotes Ptolemy's familiar qualification that the stars exert their influence *per aliud et per accidens* and that "the wise man rules the stars." Properties of inferior objects may be used by man to counteract the effects of the constellations, or imaginations of the mind may operate to weaken their force. The author then argues that fate as he has defined it is knowable, in other words that the art of astrology is practicable, that the influence of the stars can be discerned and measured. He goes so far as to defend the assertion of Ptolemy that "when the luminaries are in the head of Algon, that is, of the Gorgon, if Mars shines in hostile aspect, the child then born will be mutilated of hands and feet, and crucified."

Contradictions between *De fato* and other works of Aquinas. The *De fato* seems at variance with the opinions of Aquinas as expressed elsewhere upon the following points. It correctly cites Boethius' *De consolatione philosophiae* that the incident of finding hidden treasure while digging a grave is an example of "the inevitable connection of causes which proceeds from the fount of the knowledge of God," whereas Aquinas incorrectly cited it as an illustration of an accidental event. Again, the author of *De fato* regards the story of the Magi and the star of Bethlehem as an evidence of the truth of astrology. He also seems to believe that "intelligence through the motion of the sky rules and causes the intellectual operations of the soul," which Aquinas refused to concede. *De fato* also explains fascination somewhat differently from Aquinas. It appears to agree with him that the soul of the person exercising the power of fascination affects the person fascinated through the sense of sight; but it suggests that the soul of the fascinator has been endowed by the stars with power over the soul of the fascinated, whereas

Aquinas denied that certain men were made magicians by their nativities. Finally *De fato* does not, like Aquinas, reject astrological images, but declares that celestial influence is received by artificial as well as by natural objects, "and therefore the figures of magic images are engraved according to the constellations."

This is the end of this publication.

Any remaining blank pages are for our book binding
requirements and are blank on purpose.

To search thousands of interesting publications like this one,
please remember to visit our website at:

http://www.kessinger.net

Printed in the United States
47028LVS00005B/142

9 781425 455149